Great getting-up morning

Trad. arranged K.B.

'Getting-up' may be sung as 'Get'n'-up'

Choral Programme Series

Consultant Editor: Simon Halsey

J. Loren

Feel the Spirit!

FIVE CONTEMPORARY GOSPEL CHORUSES

GREAT GETTING-UP MORNING · NOBODY KNOWS
PUT ON THE ARMOUR · STEAL AWAY
EV'RY TIME I FEEL THE SPIRIT

(SATB unacc. & SATB/Piano)
ARRANGED BY KEN BURTON

As sung by The London Adventist Chorale
(Sainsbury's Choir of the Year 1995)

FABER *ff* MUSIC

£4·99

CONTENTS

INTRODUCTION

Gospel music is a vibrant blend of African music and European hymns and has its roots in the 'spiritual', the traditional folk music of the Afro-American population of the Deep South of America in the 18th and 19th centuries. It expresses everyday emotions and the fundamental message is of freedom and deliverance. The originators of this musical style, then slaves, longed to be free and continually planned escapes from the houses of their masters; many of the messages in spirituals therefore have a deliberately ambiguous meaning. *Swing low, sweet chariot*, for example, was a reference to a secret underground railroad through which the slaves could escape; the 'Jordan River' symbolised struggle and oppression and 'home' or 'Heaven' is a reference both to the after life and Africa, the true home of the slaves.

The texts and original tunes in this collection are taken either from sprituals or the more optimistic gospel hymns, both of which convey strong, emotive messages. *Great getting-up morning* refers to the resurrection of the dead at the Advent of Christ (ref. New Testament, 1 Thessalonians 4: 16,17) and would be sung for encouragement, for example at a funeral. Syncopated rhythms and 'call and response' style, where the main body of the choir responds to the words and music of another group, or soloist, are common features of gospel music and characterise this setting. In contrast, the 'trouble' in *Nobody knows* was the suffering of the slaves, who were taken away from their families and isolated. The 'humming' in this arrangement, a gospel style characteristic, represents the moaning and wailing of the troubled people. Improvisation is widely used in the performance of gospel music and the solid, repetitive tenor and bass lines of *Steal away* create an ideal foundation over which other parts can improvise – the syncopated sections of the alto line are a written-out example of such improvising. *Put on the armour* and *Ev'ry time I feel the spirit* display the influence of jazz in contemporary gospel music. In the former, the voices imitate double bass and jazz wind instruments in the opening section and elsewhere, while the harmonies have much in common with the big band style of the thirties. The piano part in the latter is *obbligato* and underpins all but the slow middle section. A pianist with a good grounding in gospel style should add to this written part *ad lib*.

Performance

The music must be expressive and free, yet disciplined enough to ensure a good balance, dynamic contrast, and precise entries and cut-offs. Soloists should feel free to improvise, adding notes, pulling the rhythm around, or even treating the written melody as an outline, or guide.

Dynamics are, of course, tied to the meaning of the words and should be treated quite strictly. This should not, however, deter performers from adding their own where none is specifically indicated. Rhythms should be strictly as written except in *Put on the armour*, where swing rhythm (i.e. ♪♪ = ♩ ♪) should be used. In this piece, finger clicking on every 2nd and 4th beat is effective.

Pronunciation

Rather than "Put on de armour of de Lord" and "De devil sho' is workin' ", etc., modern English spelling is used throughout. Choirs should feel free to move as far towards 'authentic' pronunciation as is comfortable.

Ken Burton

Copyright © 1996 by Faber Music Ltd
First published in 1996 by Faber Music Ltd
3 Queen Square London WC1N 3AU
Cover design by S & M Tucker
Music processed by Chris & Gail Hinkins
Printed in England by Caligraving Ltd
All rights reserved

ISBN 0-571-51687-4

Nobody knows

Trad. arranged K.B.

* Some sopranos may sing upper alto line if necessary (to bar 16)

Put on the armour

Ken Burton

Steal away

Trad. arranged K.B.

* portamento

Ev'ry time I feel the spirit

Trad. arranged K.B.

* portamento

P28B10

* Optional solo

Feel the Spirit!

This energetic, sparkling collection, by one of Britain's leading gospel choral exponents, is a superb introduction to the genre for all choirs. Ken Burton directs the outstanding London Adventist Chorale, the Sainsbury's Choir of the Year 1995.

The Faber Music Choral Programme Series

The acclaimed Choral Programme Series is now a well-established programming tool for many choirs. The series, spanning both mixed- and upper-voice repertoire, offers a wealth of fresh material from the fifteenth century onwards.

Some other volumes for mixed voices

Johann Sebastian Bach *Great Sacred Choruses*	ISBN 0-571-51960-1
Benjamin Britten *Christ's Nativity*	ISBN 0-571-51513-4
Anton Bruckner *The Great Unaccompanied Motets*	ISBN 0-571-51764-1
Anton Bruckner *Six Sacred Choruses*	ISBN 0-571-51473-1
Antonín Dvo ák *Four Choruses*	ISBN 0-571-51326-3
Gustav Holst *Five Partsongs*	ISBN 0-571-51325-5
Paul McCartney *Liverpool Oratorio Selection*	ISBN 0-571-51433-2
Felix Mendelssohn *Four Sacred Partsongs*	ISBN 0-571-51363-8
Wolfgang Amadeus Mozart *Six Motets*	ISBN 0-571-51774-9
Henry Purcell *Five Anthems*	ISBN 0-571-51515-0
Franz Schubert *Four Partsongs*	ISBN 0-571-51250-X
Pyotr Ilyich Tchaikovsky *Masterworks of the Russian Orthodox Church*	ISBN 0-571-51640-8
Ralph Vaughan Williams *Three Choral Hymns*	ISBN 0-571-51418-9
A Christmas Celebration (edited by Peter Holman)	ISBN 0-571-51792-7
Classic Victorian Ballads (arranged by Jonathan Rathbone)	ISBN 0-571-51813-3
Fair Oriana *Madrigals in celebration of Elizabeth I*	ISBN 0-571-52117-7
Five American Folksongs (arranged by Daryl Runswick)	ISBN 0-571-51262-3
Five English Folksongs (arranged by Daryl Runswick)	ISBN 0-571-51253-4
Five Welsh Carols (arranged by Louis Halsey)	-3
French Chansons (edited by Tim Brown)	-7
Gilbert & Sullivan Choruses Volume 1 (edited by Ronald Corp)	3
Gilbert & Sullivan Choruses Volume 2 (edited by Ronald Corp)	1
Hamba Lulu *Six African Songs* (arranged by Mike Brewer)	-9
Masterpieces of the French Baroque (edited by Graham Sadler)	ISBN 0-571-51935-0
Musicke's Praier *Classic English Prayer Settings* (edited by Tim Brown)	ISBN 0-571-51899-0
Passetime with good company *Medieval Songs and Carols*	44-52033-2
Passiontide Masterworks (edited by Tim Brown)	-51747-1

£ 2·00

SHELTER
SCOTLAND

Price: Code:

To buy Faber Music publications or to find out about the full range of titles available
please contact your local music retailer or Faber Music sales enquiries:

Faber Music Ltd, Burnt Mill, Elizabeth Way, Harlow CM20 2HX. England
Tel: +44 (0)1279 82 89 82   Fax: +44 (0)1279 82 89 83
sales@fabermusic.com   www.fabermusic.com

FABER MUSIC · 3 QUEEN SQUARE · LONDON

ISBN 0-571-51687-4

9 780571 516872